Swamp Spring

Carol and Donald Carrick

Swamp Spring

The Macmillan Company, New York • Collier-Macmillan Limited, London

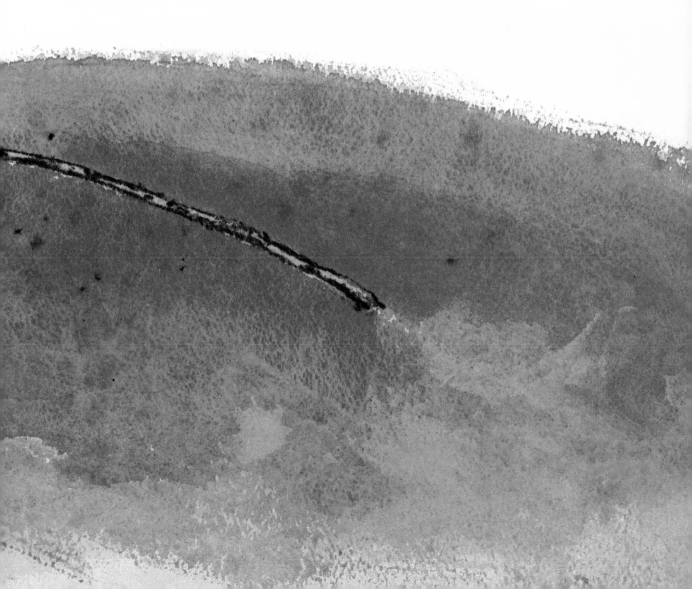

To the conservationists,
who hold back the day
when swamps exist only in books

Spring is frozen in the swamp
when the blackbird's call
rings over the ice.

Warm drizzles
on the open waters
blur reflections.

The ducks fly from the south.
They rest and dive for water weeds
before they build their nests.

Water from the melting snow, rain,
and underground springs
runs into the brook.
It stops at the beaver's dam,
and spreads across the valley.

Water sparkles in the clumps of grass.
Plant scum stains the puddles
brown and green.

Drowned trees stand
in a silent wilderness.

Snakes and frogs
sleep under logs,
in mud
and hollow trees.

Skunk cabbage
grows giant leaves
and marsh marigolds
invite the bees
to gather pollen.

A wren bobs on a swinging reed
and twitters off again.
Birds fill the air
with flying, feeding, fighting.

The animals leave their winter nests
to search for food.
New buds and leaves
make tender meals
and hide the cottontail.

The spring moon
lights the beaver's waterways.
He paddles off
to find his midnight lunch.

In the cover of the dark,
the raccoon prods
the muddy banks
for worms.

The great owl
slowly turns her head
to listen
for the chirping
of the peepers
and the rustling
in the grass.

The morning sun
warms the shallow water,
waking sleeping frogs
and fish.
New life begins
among the tangled roots.

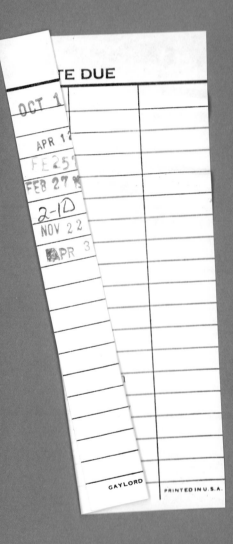